Central WPS

# Times Tables

## Key Stage 1
## For ages 5-7

# Practise & Learn

Published by CGP

Editors:
Luke Antieul
Joe Brazier
David Broadbent
Holly Poynton

Updated by Ben Train.

With thanks to Sarah Oxley for the proofreading.

ISBN: 978 1 84762 744 5

Printed by Elanders Ltd, Newcastle upon Tyne
Clipart from Corel®

# Contents

# TWO times table

Here is the two times table: ⇨

| | | | | |
|---|---|---|---|---|
| 1 | × | 2 | = | 2 |
| 2 | × | 2 | = | 4 |
| 3 | × | 2 | = | 6 |
| 4 | × | 2 | = | 8 |
| 5 | × | 2 | = | 10 |
| 6 | × | 2 | = | 12 |
| 7 | × | 2 | = | 14 |
| 8 | × | 2 | = | 16 |
| 9 | × | 2 | = | 18 |
| 10 | × | 2 | = | 20 |
| 11 | × | 2 | = | 22 |
| 12 | × | 2 | = | 24 |

Use the sets of dots to help you count to each number in the two times table.

---

Cover up the two times table above.
Then fill in the boxes.

1 × 2 = [2]

2 × [ ] = 4

[ ] × 2 = 6

4 × 2 = [ ]

[ ] × 2 = 10

6 × [ ] = 12

7 × 2 = [ ]

[ ] × 2 = 16

9 × [ ] = 18

10 × 2 = [ ]

11 × 2 = [ ]

[ ] × 2 = 24

4

The farmer's chickens are all lined up in pairs.
Count the chickens in twos. Fill in the boxes.

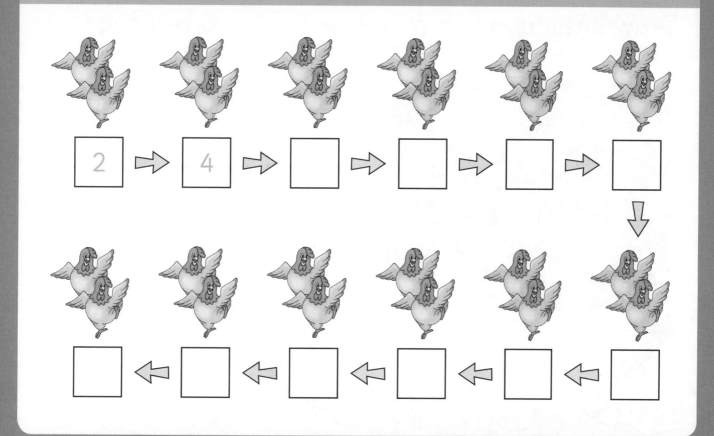

Write the number of pairs of boots in
each picture. Then write the total
number of boots in each picture

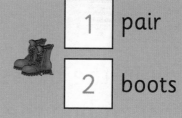

1 | pair
2 | boots

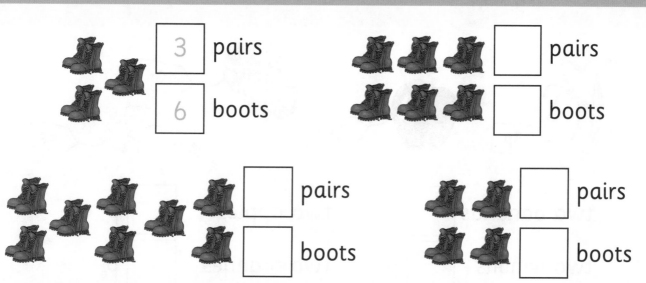

# TWO times table

Draw lines to match each lock to the correct key.

Fill in the boxes to show how much it would cost to buy the items.

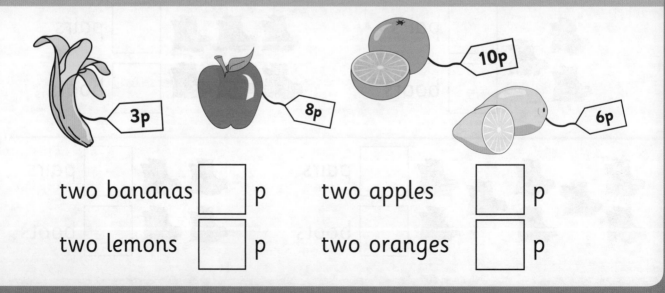

two bananas [ ] p          two apples [ ] p

two lemons [ ] p          two oranges [ ] p

6

## Write the answers in the boxes.

1. 6 cats each have 2 kittens.
   How many kittens are there in total?　☐

2. Sweets cost 2p each.
   How much does a bag of 8 sweets cost?　☐ p

3. A week has 7 days.
   How many days are there in 2 weeks?　☐

4. To make 1 cake, you need 2 eggs.  How many
   eggs will it take to make 9 cakes?　☐

## Write the answers to the questions below. See how fast you can do them all.

| | | |
|---|---|---|
| 5 × 2 = 10 | 10 × 2 = ☐ |
| ☐ × 2 = 4 | ☐ × 2 = 6 |
| 2 × 4 = ☐ | 2 × ☐ = 14 |
| 3 × 2 = ☐ | 11 × 2 = ☐ |
| ☐ × 2 = 18 | ☐ × 2 = 12 |
| 2 × ☐ = 24 | 2 × ☐ = 16 |

# FIVE times table

Here is the five times table: ⇨

Write this out three times on a separate bit of paper to help you remember it.

| | | | | |
|---|---|---|---|---|
| 1 | × | 5 | = | 5 |
| 2 | × | 5 | = | 10 |
| 3 | × | 5 | = | 15 |
| 4 | × | 5 | = | 20 |
| 5 | × | 5 | = | 25 |
| 6 | × | 5 | = | 30 |
| 7 | × | 5 | = | 35 |
| 8 | × | 5 | = | 40 |
| 9 | × | 5 | = | 45 |
| 10 | × | 5 | = | 50 |
| 11 | × | 5 | = | 55 |
| 12 | × | 5 | = | 60 |

Cover up the five times table above.
Then fill in the boxes.

1 × [5] = 5

☐ × 5 = 10

3 × 5 = ☐

4 × ☐ = 20

☐ × 5 = 25

6 × 5 = ☐

7 × ☐ = 35

☐ × 5 = 40

9 × 5 = ☐

10 × ☐ = 50

☐ × 5 = 55

12 × 5 = ☐

Draw a line from the start to the finish. You can only pass through numbers in the five times table.

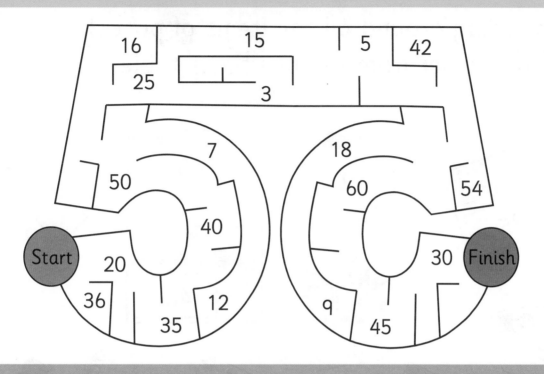

There are five muffins in each tray.
How many muffins are there in each set below?

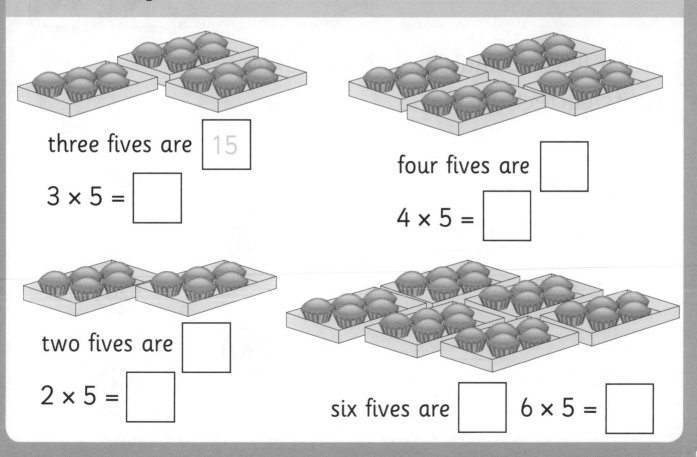

three fives are  15

$3 \times 5 = $ ☐

four fives are ☐

$4 \times 5 = $ ☐

two fives are ☐

$2 \times 5 = $ ☐

six fives are ☐    $6 \times 5 = $ ☐

# FIVE times table

Draw a ring around all the items of post that have a number from the five times table.

Draw lines to match each multiplication to its correct answer.

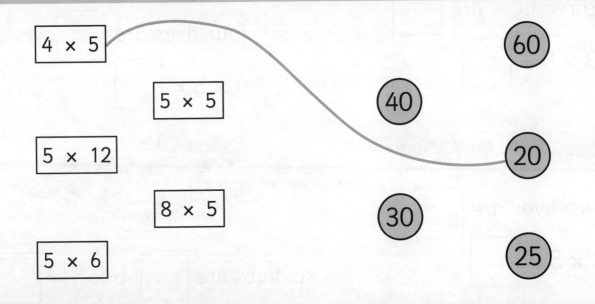

4 × 5

5 × 5

5 × 12

8 × 5

5 × 6

60

40

20

30

25

## Write the answers in the boxes.

**1** A banana costs 5p.
How much would 4 bananas cost? ☐ p

**2** A jar has 5 biscuits in it.
How many biscuits would be in 11 jars? ☐

**3** A house has 5 windows.
How many windows are there on 2 houses? ☐

**4** Jim, Sam and Jill each bought 5 puppies.
How many puppies did they buy in total? ☐

Write the answers to the questions below.
See how fast you can do them all.

$5 \times 4 = \boxed{20}$　　　$6 \times \boxed{\phantom{0}} = 30$

$\boxed{\phantom{0}} \times 5 = 35$　　　$\boxed{\phantom{0}} \times 10 = 50$

$5 \times 3 = \boxed{\phantom{0}}$　　　$5 \times \boxed{\phantom{0}} = 25$

$8 \times \boxed{\phantom{0}} = 40$　　　$12 \times 5 = \boxed{\phantom{0}}$

$\boxed{\phantom{0}} \times 5 = 45$　　　$11 \times \boxed{\phantom{0}} = 55$

$5 \times \boxed{\phantom{0}} = 10$　　　$5 \times 6 = \boxed{\phantom{0}}$

# TEN times table

Here is the ten times table:

All the answers in the ten times table end in zero — so they are all even numbers.

| | | | | |
|---|---|---|---|---|
| 1 | × | 10 | = | 10 |
| 2 | × | 10 | = | 20 |
| 3 | × | 10 | = | 30 |
| 4 | × | 10 | = | 40 |
| 5 | × | 10 | = | 50 |
| 6 | × | 10 | = | 60 |
| 7 | × | 10 | = | 70 |
| 8 | × | 10 | = | 80 |
| 9 | × | 10 | = | 90 |
| 10 | × | 10 | = | 100 |
| 11 | × | 10 | = | 110 |
| 12 | × | 10 | = | 120 |

Cover up the ten times table above.
Then fill in the boxes.

| | | | | | | | | | |
|---|---|---|---|---|---|---|---|---|---|
| 1 | × | 10 | = | 10 | | ☐ | × | 10 | = | 70 |
| 2 | × | ☐ | = | 20 | | 8 | × | ☐ | = | 80 |
| 3 | × | 10 | = | ☐ | | 9 | × | 10 | = | ☐ |
| ☐ | × | 10 | = | 40 | | ☐ | × | 10 | = | 100 |
| 5 | × | ☐ | = | 50 | | 11 | × | 10 | = | ☐ |
| 6 | × | 10 | = | ☐ | | ☐ | × | 10 | = | 120 |

12

Using numbers from the 10 times table, draw a path from the start of the hopscotch course to the finish.

|       | 50 |    | 43 |    | 15 |    | 30 | finish |
|-------|----|----|----|----|----|----|----|--------|
| start 10 | 25 | 40 | 17 | 20 | 60 | 90 | 88 | 70 |
|       | 39 |    | 80 |    | 41 |    | 55 |        |

Each jar has 10 sweets. Fill in the boxes to show how many sweets there are in each set below.

one ten is [ 10 ]

four tens are [  ]

1 × 10 = [  ]

4 × 10 = [  ]

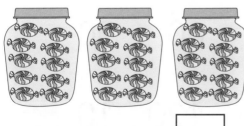   

three tens are [  ]

two tens are [  ]

3 × 10 = [  ]

2 × 10 = [  ]

13

# TEN times table

The monkey will only eat bananas with numbers that appear in the ten times table. Draw a ring around the bananas that the monkey will eat.

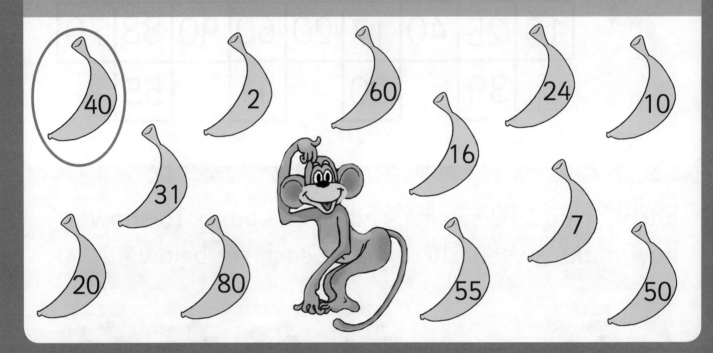

On each line, underline the number which matches the multiplication in the circle.

$11 \times 10$ → <u>110</u>   70   10   50

$9 \times 10$ → 20   80   60   90

$12 \times 10$ → 30   100   120   10

$5 \times 10$ → 20   50   40   30

Write the answers in the boxes.

1   A crate can carry 10 oranges.
    How many oranges would be in 3 crates?   ☐

2   10 children each eat 2 apples.
    How many apples are eaten in total?   ☐

3   A cup costs 10p.
    How much would 7 cups cost?   ☐ p

4   There are 4 ponies in each field.
    How many ponies are there in 10 fields?   ☐

Write the answers to the questions below.
See how fast you can do them all.

| | | |
|---|---|---|
| $5 \times 10 = \boxed{50}$ | | $12 \times 10 = \boxed{\phantom{0}}$ |
| $\boxed{\phantom{0}} \times 2 = 20$ | | $6 \times \boxed{\phantom{0}} = 60$ |
| $10 \times 7 = \boxed{\phantom{0}}$ | | $10 \times \boxed{\phantom{0}} = 40$ |
| $\boxed{\phantom{0}} \times 6 = 60$ | | $\boxed{\phantom{0}} \times 11 = 110$ |
| $8 \times \boxed{\phantom{0}} = 80$ | | $10 \times \boxed{\phantom{0}} = 80$ |
| $1 \times 10 = \boxed{\phantom{0}}$ | | $3 \times 10 = \boxed{\phantom{0}}$ |

15

# Mixed Questions

Fill in the boxes to show how many eyes there are in each line below.  2 eyes

 2 lots of 2 2 × 2 = 4

 ☐ lots of 2 ☐ × ☐ = ☐

 ☐ lots of 2 ☐ × ☐ = ☐

 ☐ lots of 2 ☐ × ☐ = ☐

Fill in the boxes to show how much it would cost to buy the items.

 8p    4p   5p

two sweets ☐ p     five bears ☐ p

five pears ☐ p      twelve sweets ☐ p

ten bears ☐ p       two pears ☐ p

# Practise and Learn

CGP

# Times Tables
# Ages 5-7
# Answers

This section shows each of the pages from the book with the answers filled in.

The pages are laid out in the same way as the book itself, so the questions can be easily marked by you, or by your child.

There are also helpful learning tips with some of the pages.

---

**4**

## TWO times table

Here is the two times table: ➡

Use the sets of dots to help you count to each number in the two times table.

| | | | | | |
|---|---|---|---|---|---|
| 1 | × | 2 | = | 2 | : |
| 2 | × | 2 | = | 4 | :: |
| 3 | × | 2 | = | 6 | ::: |
| 4 | × | 2 | = | 8 | :::: |
| 5 | × | 2 | = | 10 | ::::: |
| 6 | × | 2 | = | 12 | :::::: |
| 7 | × | 2 | = | 14 | ::::::: |
| 8 | × | 2 | = | 16 | :::::::: |
| 9 | × | 2 | = | 18 | ::::::::: |
| 10 | × | 2 | = | 20 | :::::::::: |
| 11 | × | 2 | = | 22 | ::::::::::: |
| 12 | × | 2 | = | 24 | :::::::::::: |

Cover up the two times table above.
Then fill in the boxes.

| | | | | | | | | | | |
|---|---|---|---|---|---|---|---|---|---|---|
| 1 | × | 2 | = | 2 | | 7 | × | 2 | = | 14 |
| 2 | × | 2 | = | 4 | | 8 | × | 2 | = | 16 |
| 3 | × | 2 | = | 6 | | 9 | × | 2 | = | 18 |
| 4 | × | 2 | = | 8 | | 10 | × | 2 | = | 20 |
| 5 | × | 2 | = | 10 | | 11 | × | 2 | = | 22 |
| 6 | × | 2 | = | 12 | | 12 | × | 2 | = | 24 |

4

---

**5**

The farmer's chickens are all lined up in pairs. Count the chickens in twos. Fill in the boxes.

2 ⇨ 4 ⇨ 6 ⇨ 8 ⇨ 10 ⇨ 12
⇩
24 ⇦ 22 ⇦ 20 ⇦ 18 ⇦ 16 ⇦ 14

Write the number of pairs of boots in each picture. Then write the total number of boots in each picture

1 pair
2 boots

3 pairs       6 pairs
6 boots       12 boots

8 pairs       4 pairs
16 boots      8 boots

5

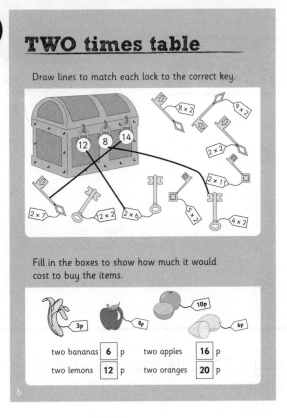

## TWO times table

Draw lines to match each lock to the correct key.

Fill in the boxes to show how much it would cost to buy the items.

two bananas **6** p     two apples **16** p

two lemons **12** p     two oranges **20** p

6

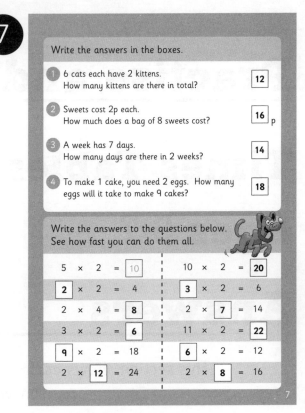

Write the answers in the boxes.

1. 6 cats each have 2 kittens. How many kittens are there in total? **12**

2. Sweets cost 2p each. How much does a bag of 8 sweets cost? **16** p

3. A week has 7 days. How many days are there in 2 weeks? **14**

4. To make 1 cake, you need 2 eggs. How many eggs will it take to make 9 cakes? **18**

Write the answers to the questions below. See how fast you can do them all.

| | | | | | | | | | |
|---|---|---|---|---|---|---|---|---|---|
| 5 | × | 2 | = | 10 | 10 | × | 2 | = | **20** |
| **2** | × | 2 | = | 4 | **3** | × | 2 | = | 6 |
| 2 | × | 4 | = | **8** | 2 | × | **7** | = | 14 |
| 3 | × | 2 | = | **6** | 11 | × | 2 | = | **22** |
| **9** | × | 2 | = | 18 | **6** | × | 2 | = | 12 |
| 2 | × | **12** | = | 24 | 2 | × | **8** | = | 16 |

7

## FIVE times table

Here is the five times table: ↘

Write this out three times on a separate bit of paper to help you remember it.

| | | | | |
|---|---|---|---|---|
| 1 | × | 5 | = | 5 |
| 2 | × | 5 | = | 10 |
| 3 | × | 5 | = | 15 |
| 4 | × | 5 | = | 20 |
| 5 | × | 5 | = | 25 |
| 6 | × | 5 | = | 30 |
| 7 | × | 5 | = | 35 |
| 8 | × | 5 | = | 40 |
| 9 | × | 5 | = | 45 |
| 10 | × | 5 | = | 50 |
| 11 | × | 5 | = | 55 |
| 12 | × | 5 | = | 60 |

Cover up the five times table above. Then fill in the boxes.

| | | | | | | | | | |
|---|---|---|---|---|---|---|---|---|---|
| 1 | × | 5 | = | 5 | 7 | × | **5** | = | 35 |
| **2** | × | 5 | = | 10 | **8** | × | 5 | = | 40 |
| 3 | × | 5 | = | **15** | 9 | × | 5 | = | **45** |
| 4 | × | **5** | = | 20 | 10 | × | **5** | = | 50 |
| **5** | × | 5 | = | 25 | **11** | × | 5 | = | 55 |
| 6 | × | 5 | = | **30** | 12 | × | 5 | = | **60** |

8

Draw a line from the start to the finish. You can only pass through numbers in the five times table.

There are five muffins in each tray. How many muffins are there in each set below?

three fives are 15

3 × 5 = **15**

four fives are **20**

4 × 5 = **20**

two fives are **10**

2 × 5 = **10**

six fives are **30**   6 × 5 = **30**

9

You can help your child remember the five times table by showing them that every number always ends in a 5 or a 0.

## 10 — FIVE times table

Draw a ring around all the items of post that have a number from the five times table.

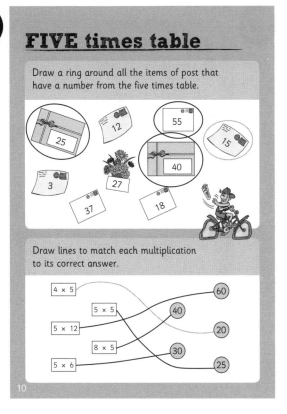

Draw lines to match each multiplication to its correct answer.

| | | |
|---|---|---|
| 4 × 5 | | 60 |
| 5 × 5 | | 40 |
| 5 × 12 | | 20 |
| 8 × 5 | | 30 |
| 5 × 6 | | 25 |

## 11

Write the answers in the boxes.

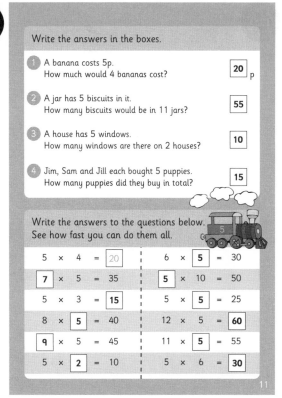

1. A banana costs 5p.
How much would 4 bananas cost? **20** p

2. A jar has 5 biscuits in it.
How many biscuits would be in 11 jars? **55**

3. A house has 5 windows.
How many windows are there on 2 houses? **10**

4. Jim, Sam and Jill each bought 5 puppies.
How many puppies did they buy in total? **15**

Write the answers to the questions below. See how fast you can do them all.

| | | | | | | | | | | | |
|---|---|---|---|---|---|---|---|---|---|---|---|
| 5 | × | 4 | = | 20 | | 6 | × | **5** | = | 30 |
| **7** | × | 5 | = | 35 | | **5** | × | 10 | = | 50 |
| 5 | × | 3 | = | **15** | | 5 | × | **5** | = | 25 |
| 8 | × | **5** | = | 40 | | 12 | × | 5 | = | **60** |
| **9** | × | 5 | = | 45 | | 11 | × | **5** | = | 55 |
| 5 | × | **2** | = | 10 | | 5 | × | 6 | = | **30** |

Questions without visual prompts can be a challenge for some children. You can help by talking them through an example and showing them the calculation they need to solve.

## 12 — TEN times table

Here is the ten times table:

| | | | | |
|---|---|---|---|---|
| 1 | × | 10 | = | 10 |
| 2 | × | 10 | = | 20 |
| 3 | × | 10 | = | 30 |
| 4 | × | 10 | = | 40 |
| 5 | × | 10 | = | 50 |
| 6 | × | 10 | = | 60 |
| 7 | × | 10 | = | 70 |
| 8 | × | 10 | = | 80 |
| 9 | × | 10 | = | 90 |
| 10 | × | 10 | = | 100 |
| 11 | × | 10 | = | 110 |
| 12 | × | 10 | = | 120 |

All the answers in the ten times table end in zero — so they are all even numbers.

Cover up the ten times table above. Then fill in the boxes.

| | | | | | | | | | | |
|---|---|---|---|---|---|---|---|---|---|---|
| **1** | × | 10 | = | 10 | | **7** | × | 10 | = | 70 |
| 2 | × | **10** | = | 20 | | 8 | × | **10** | = | 80 |
| 3 | × | 10 | = | **30** | | 9 | × | 10 | = | **90** |
| **4** | × | 10 | = | 40 | | **10** | × | 10 | = | 100 |
| 5 | × | **10** | = | 50 | | 11 | × | 10 | = | **110** |
| 6 | × | 10 | = | **60** | | **12** | × | 10 | = | 120 |

## 13

Using numbers from the 10 times table, draw a path from the start of the hopscotch course to the finish.

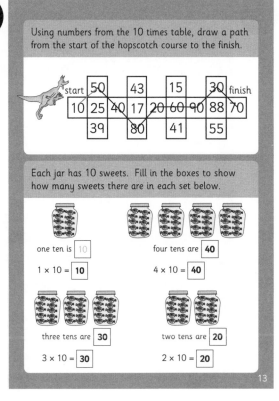

Each jar has 10 sweets. Fill in the boxes to show how many sweets there are in each set below.

one ten is **10**

$1 × 10 =$ **10**

four tens are **40**

$4 × 10 =$ **40**

three tens are **30**

$3 × 10 =$ **30**

two tens are **20**

$2 × 10 =$ **20**

# TEN times table

The monkey will only eat bananas with numbers that appear in the ten times table. Draw a ring around the bananas that the monkey will eat.

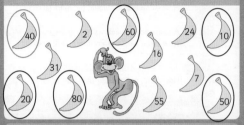

40 · 2 · 60 · 24 · 10 · 16 · 31 · 7 · 20 · 80 · 55 · 50

On each line, underline the number which matches the multiplication in the circle.

11 × 10 ⟶ <u>110</u>  70  10  50

9 × 10 ⟶  20  80  60  <u>90</u>

12 × 10 ⟶  30  100  <u>120</u>  10

5 × 10 ⟶  20  <u>50</u>  40  30

Write the answers in the boxes.

1. A crate can carry 10 oranges.
How many oranges would be in 3 crates? **30**

2. 10 children each eat 2 apples.
How many apples are eaten in total? **20**

3. A cup costs 10p.
How much would 7 cups cost? **70** p

4. There are 4 ponies in each field.
How many ponies are there in 10 fields? **40**

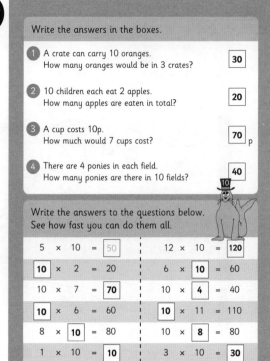

Write the answers to the questions below.
See how fast you can do them all.

| | | | | | | | | | | |
|---|---|---|---|---|---|---|---|---|---|---|
| 5 | × | 10 | = | 50 | | 12 | × | 10 | = | **120** |
| **10** | × | 2 | = | 20 | | 6 | × | **10** | = | 60 |
| 10 | × | 7 | = | **70** | | 10 | × | **4** | = | 40 |
| **10** | × | 6 | = | 60 | | **10** | × | 11 | = | 110 |
| 8 | × | **10** | = | 80 | | 10 | × | **8** | = | 80 |
| 1 | × | 10 | = | **10** | | 3 | × | 10 | = | **30** |

# Mixed Questions

Fill in the boxes to show how many eyes there are in each line below. 2 eyes

2 lots of 2    2 × 2 = 4

4 lots of 2    4 × 2 = 8

3 lots of 2    3 × 2 = 6

5 lots of 2    5 × 2 = 10

Fill in the boxes to show how much it would cost to buy the items.

8p · 4p · 5p

two sweets    **10** p    five bears    **40** p

five pears    **20** p    twelve sweets    **60** p

ten bears    **80** p    two pears    **8** p

Colour in numbers in the five times table.
See if you can spot a pattern.

| 1 | 2 | 3 | 4 | 5 | 6 | 7 | 8 | 9 | 10 |
|---|---|---|---|---|---|---|---|---|---|
| 11 | 12 | 13 | 14 | 15 | 16 | 17 | 18 | 19 | 20 |
| 21 | 22 | 23 | 24 | 25 | 26 | 27 | 28 | 29 | 30 |
| 31 | 32 | 33 | 34 | 35 | 36 | 37 | 38 | 39 | 40 |
| 41 | 42 | 43 | 44 | 45 | 46 | 47 | 48 | 49 | 50 |
| 51 | 52 | 53 | 54 | 55 | 56 | 57 | 58 | 59 | 60 |

Fill in the empty circles to finish the number wheel.

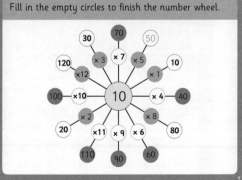

30 · 70 · 50 · 120 · ×3 · ×7 · ×5 · 10 · ×12 · ×1 · 100 · ×10 · 10 · × 4 · 40 · 20 · × 2 · × 8 · 80 · ×11 · × 9 · × 6 · 110 · 90 · 60

If your child is confused by these pages, make sure they understand that the questions are on a mixture of the times tables.

# Mixed Questions

Draw a line from the start to the finish.
Only go through numbers in the two times table.

Start ⟹
| 8 | 3 | 27 | 15 | 19 |
|---|---|----|----|----|
| 4 | 23 | 13 | 1 | 11 |
| 18 | 12 | 19 | 21 | 3 |
| 19 | 24 | 9 | 17 | 7 |
| 5 | 6 | 2 | 20 | 10 | ⟹ Finish

Colour in each part of the picture that
has a number in the five times table.

---

Write the answers in the boxes.

1. A ball costs 10p.
   How much would 5 balls cost? **50** p

2. Ben eats 2 oranges each day.
   How many oranges would he eat in 6 days? **12**

3. There are 10 eggs in 1 box.
   How many eggs are there in 3 boxes? **30**

4. An owl has 2 eyes.
   How many eyes would 8 owls have? **16**

Write the answers to the questions below.
See how fast you can do them all.

| | | | | | | |
|---|---|---|---|---|---|---|
| 7 × 2 = 14 | | 12 × 10 = **120** |
| **2** × 9 = 18 | | **5** × 8 = 40 |
| 5 × **5** = 25 | | 10 × **9** = 90 |
| 5 × 11 = **55** | | 4 × 2 = **8** |
| 1 × **10** = 10 | | **3** × 5 = 15 |
| **4** × 5 = 20 | | 5 × **6** = 30 |

If your child enjoys seeing how fast they
can complete the calculations above, try
timing them to see how fast they can write
out or recite some of their times tables.

---

# THREE times table

Here is the three
times table: ⟹

See if you can
write down
the three times
table without
looking. Then
get someone to
check it for you.

| 1 × 3 = 3 |
|---|
| 2 × 3 = 6 |
| 3 × 3 = 9 |
| 4 × 3 = 12 |
| 5 × 3 = 15 |
| 6 × 3 = 18 |
| 7 × 3 = 21 |
| 8 × 3 = 24 |
| 9 × 3 = 27 |
| 10 × 3 = 30 |
| 11 × 3 = 33 |
| 12 × 3 = 36 |

Cover up the three times table above.
Then fill in the boxes.

| | | | | | | |
|---|---|---|---|---|---|---|
| 1 × 3 = 3 | | 7 × 3 = **21** |
| 2 × 3 = **6** | | **8** × 3 = 24 |
| **3** × 3 = 9 | | **9** × 3 = 27 |
| 4 × 3 = **12** | | 10 × 3 = **30** |
| **5** × 3 = 15 | | **11** × 3 = 33 |
| **6** × 3 = 18 | | 12 × 3 = **36** |

---

Colour in the numbers in the three times table.
See if you can spot a pattern.

| 1 | 2 | 3 | 4 | 5 | 6 |
|---|---|---|---|---|---|
| 7 | 8 | 9 | 10 | 11 | 12 |
| 13 | 14 | 15 | 16 | 17 | 18 |
| 19 | 20 | 21 | 22 | 23 | 24 |
| 25 | 26 | 27 | 28 | 29 | 30 |
| 31 | 32 | 33 | 34 | 35 | 36 |

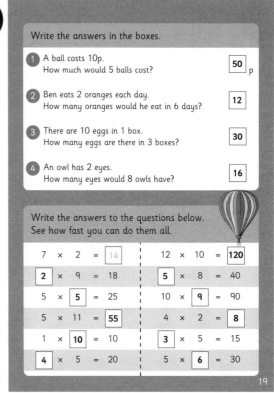

An ice-cream cone has three scoops. Fill in the boxes
to show how many scoops there are in total.

5 cones   5 × 3 = 15

9 cones   9 × 3 = 27

7 cones   7 × 3 = 21

4 cones   4 × 3 = 12

## THREE times table

Fill in the boxes to complete the multiplications.

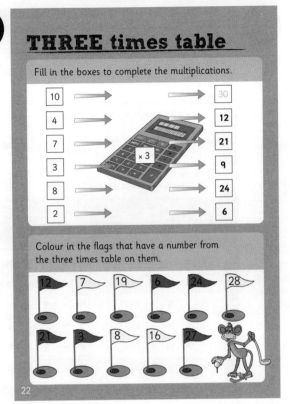

| | |
|---|---|
| 10 → | → 30 |
| 4 → | → 12 |
| 7 → | → 21 |
| 3 → | → 9 |
| 8 → | → 24 |
| 2 → | → 6 |

(× 3)

Colour in the flags that have a number from the three times table on them.

12  7  19  6  24  28
21  3  8  16  27

---

Write the answers in the boxes.

1. A monkey eats 3 bananas a day.
   How many bananas would it eat in 3 days? **9**

2. A pencil costs 9p.
   How much would 3 pencils cost? **27** p

3. A fish tank can hold 7 fish.
   How many fish would fit in 3 tanks? **21**

4. A triangle has 3 points.
   How many points are there on 6 triangles? **18**

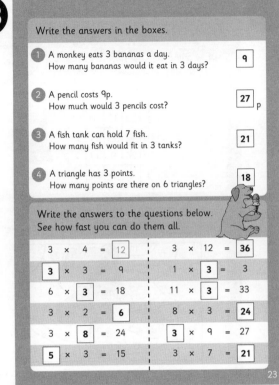

Write the answers to the questions below.
See how fast you can do them all.

| | | |
|---|---|---|
| 3 × 4 = 12 | 3 × 12 = **36** |
| **3** × 3 = 9 | 1 × **3** = 3 |
| 6 × **3** = 18 | 11 × **3** = 33 |
| 3 × 2 = **6** | 8 × 3 = **24** |
| 3 × **8** = 24 | **3** × 9 = 27 |
| **5** × 3 = 15 | 3 × 7 = **21** |

23

---

## FOUR times table

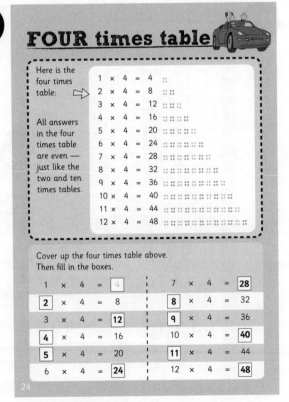

Here is the four times table:

| | | | |
|---|---|---|---|
| 1 × 4 = 4 |
| 2 × 4 = 8 |
| 3 × 4 = 12 |
| 4 × 4 = 16 |
| 5 × 4 = 20 |
| 6 × 4 = 24 |
| 7 × 4 = 28 |
| 8 × 4 = 32 |
| 9 × 4 = 36 |
| 10 × 4 = 40 |
| 11 × 4 = 44 |
| 12 × 4 = 48 |

All answers in the four times table are even — just like the two and ten times tables.

Cover up the four times table above.
Then fill in the boxes.

| | | |
|---|---|---|
| 1 × 4 = 4 | 7 × 4 = **28** |
| **2** × 4 = 8 | **8** × 4 = 32 |
| 3 × 4 = **12** | **9** × 4 = 36 |
| **4** × 4 = 16 | 10 × 4 = **40** |
| **5** × 4 = 20 | **11** × 4 = 44 |
| 6 × 4 = **24** | 12 × 4 = **48** |

24

---

Draw a line from the start to the finish. Only go through numbers in the four times table.

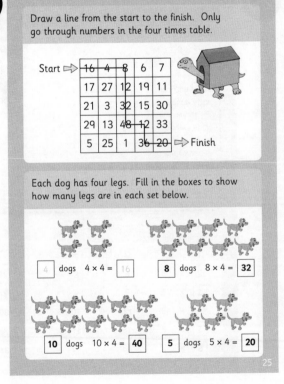

Start ⇒
| 16 | 4 | 8 | 6 | 7 |
|---|---|---|---|---|
| 17 | 27 | 12 | 19 | 11 |
| 21 | 3 | 32 | 15 | 30 |
| 29 | 13 | 48 | 12 | 33 |
| 5 | 25 | 1 | 36 | 20 |
⇒ Finish

Each dog has four legs. Fill in the boxes to show how many legs are in each set below.

**4** dogs  4 × 4 = 16

**8** dogs  8 × 4 = **32**

**10** dogs  10 × 4 = **40**

**5** dogs  5 × 4 = **20**

25

---

If your child has made a few mistakes, remind them to double check their work next time — it's a really good habit for them to get in to.

## 26

### FOUR times table

Solve the multiplications below.
Each answer matches up with a letter.
Use the letters to crack the code.

4 × 4   4 × 3   4 × 9   9 × 4        6 × 4   4 × 11   2 × 4   3 × 4
**W**   E   **L**   **L**        **D**   **O**   **N**   **E**

| Number | 12 | 24 | 8 | 16 | 44 | 36 |
|--------|----|----|----|----|----|----|
| Letter | E | . D | N | W | O | L |

Colour in the wedges on the dartboard which appear in the four times table.

## 27

Write the answers in the boxes.

1. A car has 4 wheels.
How many wheels would 12 cars have?  **48**

2. A square has 4 sides.
How many sides would 4 squares have?  **16**

3. 4 friends each have 3 buns.
How many buns do they have in total?  **12**

4. A ruler costs 4p.
How much would 6 rulers cost?  **24** p

Write the answers to the questions below.
See how fast you can do them all.

| | | |
|---|---|---|
| 7 × 4 = 28 | 4 × 4 = **16** |
| **4** × 3 = 12 | **8** × 4 = 32 |
| 4 × **6** = 24 | 10 × **4** = 40 |
| 4 × 2 = **8** | 12 × 4 = **48** |
| 9 × **4** = 36 | **4** × 1 = 4 |
| **4** × 5 = 20 | 4 × **11** = 44 |

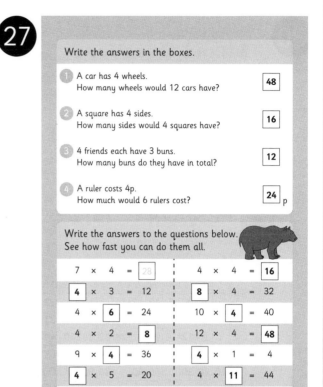

## 28

### Mixed Questions

Colour in every number that is in the two times table. See if you can spot a pattern.

| 1 | 2 | 3 | 4 | 5 |
|---|---|---|---|---|
| 6 | 7 | 8 | 9 | 10 |
| 11 | 12 | 13 | 14 | 15 |
| 16 | 17 | 18 | 19 | 20 |
| 21 | 22 | 23 | 24 | 25 |

Draw a ring around the multiplication that matches each number on the left.

| 35 | (7 × 5) | 10 × 3 | 8 × 4 | 10 × 7 |
| 15 | (3 × 5) | 10 × 4 | 3 × 7 | 5 × 9 |
| 30 | 4 × 3 | 3 × 9 | 8 × 5 | (5 × 6) |
| 27 | 4 × 4 | 3 × 7 | (3 × 9) | 8 × 2 |
| 8 | 3 × 1 | (2 × 4) | 2 × 3 | 5 × 5 |
| 33 | (11 × 3) | 3 × 8 | 2 × 10 | 7 × 3 |

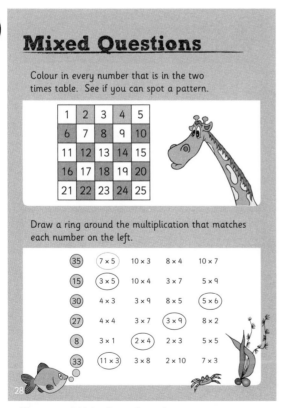

## 29

Fill in the boxes to show each number on the clock multiplied by 5.

Fill in the boxes to show how many legs are in each set below.  3 legs

3 lots of 3   3 × 3 = 9
2 lots of 3   **2** × **3** = **6**
4 lots of 3   **4** × **3** = **12**
1 lot of 3   **1** × **3** = **3**

If your child identifies the correct multiplication straight away, encourage them to work out the answers for each multiplication for more practice.

## Mixed Questions

Work out the answers to the multiplications below.
Use the key to colour the picture in.

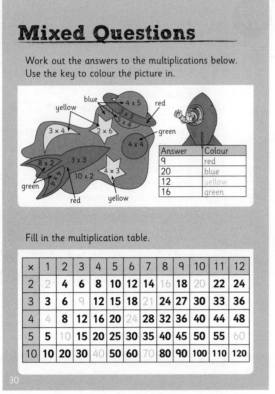

| Answer | Colour |
|---|---|
| 9 | red |
| 20 | blue |
| 12 | yellow |
| 16 | green |

Fill in the multiplication table.

| × | 1 | 2 | 3 | 4 | 5 | 6 | 7 | 8 | 9 | 10 | 11 | 12 |
|---|---|---|---|---|---|---|---|---|---|---|---|---|
| 2 | 2 | 4 | 6 | 8 | 10 | 12 | 14 | 16 | 18 | 20 | 22 | 24 |
| 3 | 3 | 6 | 9 | 12 | 15 | 18 | 21 | 24 | 27 | 30 | 33 | 36 |
| 4 | 4 | 8 | 12 | 16 | 20 | 24 | 28 | 32 | 36 | 40 | 44 | 48 |
| 5 | 5 | 10 | 15 | 20 | 25 | 30 | 35 | 40 | 45 | 50 | 55 | 60 |
| 10 | 10 | 20 | 30 | 40 | 50 | 60 | 70 | 80 | 90 | 100 | 110 | 120 |

These pages are a great way to spot which of the times tables your child is least confident with. If you find gaps in their knowledge, revisit the relevant pages.

Draw a line from the start to the finish. Only go through numbers in the ten times table.

Start ⇨

| 10 | 5 | 23 | 29 | 19 |
|---|---|---|---|---|
| 70 | 85 | 57 | 1 | 16 |
| 40 | 30 | 14 | 50 | 70 |
| 29 | 90 | 23 | 10 | 75 |
| 25 | 20 | 60 | 80 | 35 |

⇨ Finish

Colour in the balls that have a number from the four times table.

44   36   18   32

8   7   24   3

38   26   10

## Mixed Questions

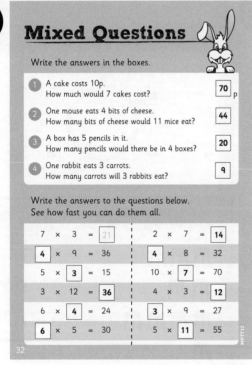

Write the answers in the boxes.

1. A cake costs 10p.
   How much would 7 cakes cost?   **70** p

2. One mouse eats 4 bits of cheese.
   How many bits of cheese would 11 mice eat?   **44**

3. A box has 5 pencils in it.
   How many pencils would there be in 4 boxes?   **20**

4. One rabbit eats 3 carrots.
   How many carrots will 3 rabbits eat?   **9**

Write the answers to the questions below.
See how fast you can do them all.

| 7 × 3 = 21 | 2 × 7 = **14** |
|---|---|
| **4** × 9 = 36 | **4** × 8 = 32 |
| 5 × **3** = 15 | 10 × **7** = 70 |
| 3 × 12 = **36** | 4 × 3 = **12** |
| 6 × **4** = 24 | **3** × 9 = 27 |
| **6** × 5 = 30 | 5 × **11** = 55 |

MPTT12

Colour in numbers in the five times table.
See if you can spot a pattern.

| 1 | 2 | 3 | 4 | 5 | 6 | 7 | 8 | 9 | 10 |
|---|---|---|---|---|---|---|---|---|---|
| 11 | 12 | 13 | 14 | 15 | 16 | 17 | 18 | 19 | 20 |
| 21 | 22 | 23 | 24 | 25 | 26 | 27 | 28 | 29 | 30 |
| 31 | 32 | 33 | 34 | 35 | 36 | 37 | 38 | 39 | 40 |
| 41 | 42 | 43 | 44 | 45 | 46 | 47 | 48 | 49 | 50 |
| 51 | 52 | 53 | 54 | 55 | 56 | 57 | 58 | 59 | 60 |

Fill in the empty circles to finish the number wheel.

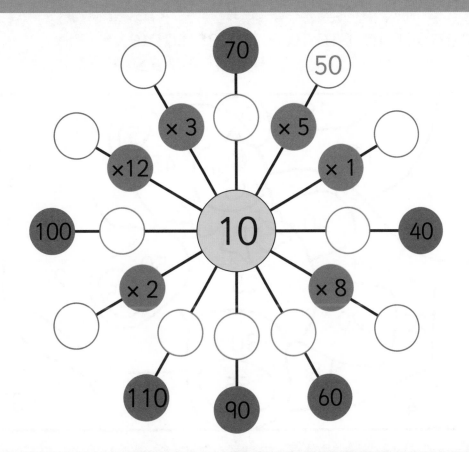

17

# Mixed Questions

Draw a line from the start to the finish.
Only go through numbers in the two times table.

Start ⇨

| 8 | 3 | 27 | 15 | 19 |
|---|---|----|----|----|
| 4 | 23 | 13 | 1 | 11 |
| 18 | 12 | 19 | 21 | 3 |
| 19 | 24 | 9 | 17 | 7 |
| 5 | 6 | 2 | 20 | 10 |

⇨ Finish

Colour in each part of the picture that
has a number in the five times table.

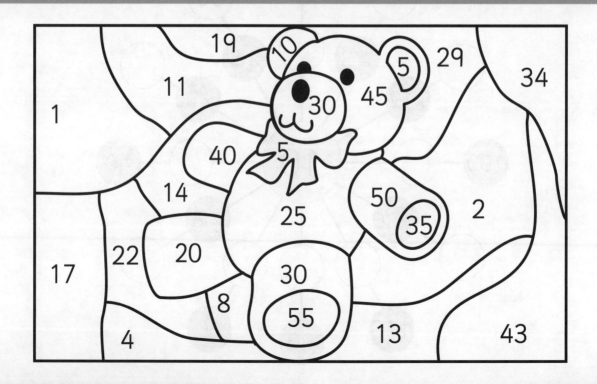

19  10  5  29
11          34
1       30  45
    40  5
    14      50  2
        25      35
22  20
17      30
    8
        55
4       13      43

18

Write the answers in the boxes.

**1** A ball costs 10p.
How much would 5 balls cost?  p

**2** Ben eats 2 oranges each day.
How many oranges would he eat in 6 days?

**3** There are 10 eggs in 1 box.
How many eggs are there in 3 boxes?

**4** An owl has 2 eyes.
How many eyes would 8 owls have?

Write the answers to the questions below.
See how fast you can do them all.

$7 \times 2 = \boxed{14}$          $12 \times 10 = \boxed{\phantom{0}}$

$\boxed{\phantom{0}} \times 9 = 18$          $\boxed{\phantom{0}} \times 8 = 40$

$5 \times \boxed{\phantom{0}} = 25$          $10 \times \boxed{\phantom{0}} = 90$

$5 \times 11 = \boxed{\phantom{0}}$          $4 \times 2 = \boxed{\phantom{0}}$

$1 \times \boxed{\phantom{0}} = 10$          $\boxed{\phantom{0}} \times 5 = 15$

$\boxed{\phantom{0}} \times 5 = 20$          $5 \times \boxed{\phantom{0}} = 30$

19

# THREE times table

Here is the three times table:

See if you can write down the three times table without looking. Then get someone to check it for you.

| | | | | | |
|---|---|---|---|---|---|
| 1 | × | 3 | = | 3 | |
| 2 | × | 3 | = | 6 | |
| 3 | × | 3 | = | 9 | |
| 4 | × | 3 | = | 12 | |
| 5 | × | 3 | = | 15 | |
| 6 | × | 3 | = | 18 | |
| 7 | × | 3 | = | 21 | |
| 8 | × | 3 | = | 24 | |
| 9 | × | 3 | = | 27 | |
| 10 | × | 3 | = | 30 | |
| 11 | × | 3 | = | 33 | |
| 12 | × | 3 | = | 36 | |

Cover up the three times table above.
Then fill in the boxes.

| | | | | | | | | | | |
|---|---|---|---|---|---|---|---|---|---|---|
| 1 | × | 3 | = | 3 | | 7 | × | 3 | = | ☐ |
| 2 | × | 3 | = | ☐ | | ☐ | × | 3 | = | 24 |
| ☐ | × | 3 | = | 9 | | ☐ | × | 3 | = | 27 |
| 4 | × | 3 | = | ☐ | | 10 | × | 3 | = | ☐ |
| ☐ | × | 3 | = | 15 | | ☐ | × | 3 | = | 33 |
| ☐ | × | 3 | = | 18 | | 12 | × | 3 | = | ☐ |

Colour in the numbers in the three times table.
See if you can spot a pattern.

| 1 | 2 | 3 | 4 | 5 | 6 |
|---|---|---|---|---|---|
| 7 | 8 | 9 | 10 | 11 | 12 |
| 13 | 14 | 15 | 16 | 17 | 18 |
| 19 | 20 | 21 | 22 | 23 | 24 |
| 25 | 26 | 27 | 28 | 29 | 30 |
| 31 | 32 | 33 | 34 | 35 | 36 |

An ice-cream cone has three scoops.  Fill in the boxes
to show how many scoops there are in total.

5 cones    5 × 3 = 15

☐ cones    9 × 3 = ☐

☐ cones    7 × 3 = ☐

☐ cones    4 × 3 = ☐

21

# THREE times table

## Fill in the boxes to complete the multiplications.

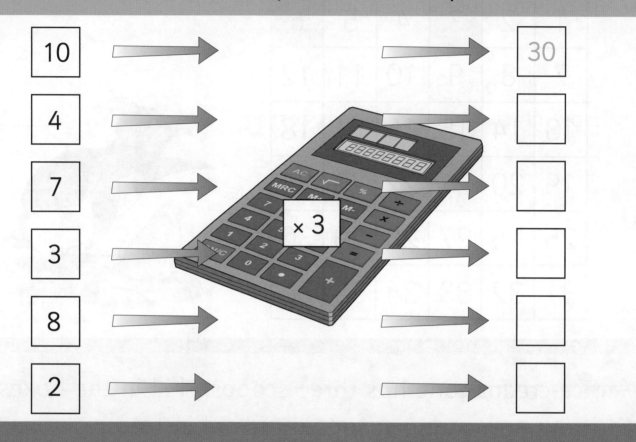

| | × 3 | |
|---|---|---|
| 10 | → | 30 |
| 4 | → | |
| 7 | → | |
| 3 | → | |
| 8 | → | |
| 2 | → | |

## Colour in the flags that have a number from the three times table on them.

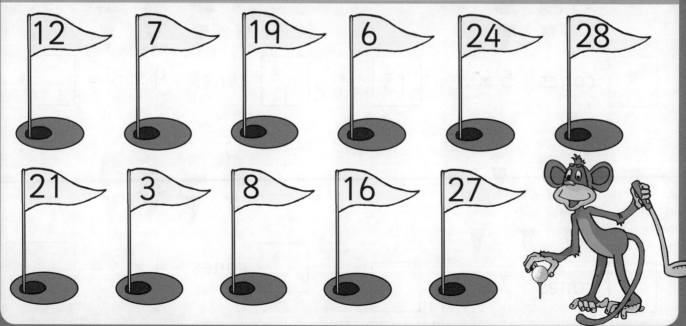

12  7  19  6  24  28

21  3  8  16  27

## Write the answers in the boxes.

**1** A monkey eats 3 bananas a day.
How many bananas would it eat in 3 days?

**2** A pencil costs 9p.
How much would 3 pencils cost?  p

**3** A fish tank can hold 7 fish.
How many fish would fit in 3 tanks?

**4** A triangle has 3 points.
How many points are there on 6 triangles?

## Write the answers to the questions below. See how fast you can do them all.

| | | | | |
|---|---|---|---|---|
| 3 × 4 = 12 | | 3 × 12 = ☐ |
| ☐ × 3 = 9 | | 1 × ☐ = 3 |
| 6 × ☐ = 18 | | 11 × ☐ = 33 |
| 3 × 2 = ☐ | | 8 × 3 = ☐ |
| 3 × ☐ = 24 | | ☐ × 9 = 27 |
| ☐ × 3 = 15 | | 3 × 7 = ☐ |

23

# FOUR times table

Here is the four times table: ➡

| | | | | | |
|---|---|---|---|---|---|
| 1 | × | 4 | = | 4 | ❖ |
| 2 | × | 4 | = | 8 | ❖ ❖ |
| 3 | × | 4 | = | 12 | ❖ ❖ ❖ |
| 4 | × | 4 | = | 16 | ❖ ❖ ❖ ❖ |
| 5 | × | 4 | = | 20 | ❖ ❖ ❖ ❖ ❖ |
| 6 | × | 4 | = | 24 | ❖ ❖ ❖ ❖ ❖ ❖ |
| 7 | × | 4 | = | 28 | ❖ ❖ ❖ ❖ ❖ ❖ ❖ |
| 8 | × | 4 | = | 32 | ❖ ❖ ❖ ❖ ❖ ❖ ❖ ❖ |
| 9 | × | 4 | = | 36 | ❖ ❖ ❖ ❖ ❖ ❖ ❖ ❖ ❖ |
| 10 | × | 4 | = | 40 | ❖ ❖ ❖ ❖ ❖ ❖ ❖ ❖ ❖ ❖ |
| 11 | × | 4 | = | 44 | ❖ ❖ ❖ ❖ ❖ ❖ ❖ ❖ ❖ ❖ ❖ |
| 12 | × | 4 | = | 48 | ❖ ❖ ❖ ❖ ❖ ❖ ❖ ❖ ❖ ❖ ❖ ❖ |

All answers in the four times table are even — just like the two and ten times tables.

Cover up the four times table above.
Then fill in the boxes.

| | | | | |
|---|---|---|---|---|
| 1 | × | 4 | = | 4 |
| ☐ | × | 4 | = | 8 |
| 3 | × | 4 | = | ☐ |
| ☐ | × | 4 | = | 16 |
| ☐ | × | 4 | = | 20 |
| 6 | × | 4 | = | ☐ |

| | | | | |
|---|---|---|---|---|
| 7 | × | 4 | = | ☐ |
| ☐ | × | 4 | = | 32 |
| ☐ | × | 4 | = | 36 |
| 10 | × | 4 | = | ☐ |
| ☐ | × | 4 | = | 44 |
| 12 | × | 4 | = | ☐ |

24

Draw a line from the start to the finish. Only go through numbers in the four times table.

Start ⇨

| 16 | 4 | 8 | 6 | 7 |
|----|----|----|----|----|
| 17 | 27 | 12 | 19 | 11 |
| 21 | 3 | 32 | 15 | 30 |
| 29 | 13 | 48 | 12 | 33 |
| 5 | 25 | 1 | 36 | 20 |

⇨ Finish

Each dog has four legs. Fill in the boxes to show how many legs are in each set below.

4 dogs   4 × 4 = 16

☐ dogs   8 × 4 = ☐

☐ dogs   10 × 4 = ☐

☐ dogs   5 × 4 = ☐

25

# FOUR times table

Solve the multiplications below.
Each answer matches up with a letter.
Use the letters to crack the code.

$4 \times 4$   $4 \times 3$   $4 \times 9$   $9 \times 4$      $6 \times 4$   $4 \times 11$   $2 \times 4$   $3 \times 4$

___   E   ___   ___   ___      ___   ___   ___   ___

| Number | 12 | 24 | 8 | 16 | 44 | 36 |
|--------|----|----|----|----|----|----|
| Letter | E | D | N | W | O | L |

TOP SECRET

Colour in the wedges on the dartboard which appear in the four times table.

6   38
24      8
35      16
12   19

26

Write the answers in the boxes.

1. A car has 4 wheels.
   How many wheels would 12 cars have?
   ☐

2. A square has 4 sides.
   How many sides would 4 squares have?
   ☐

3. 4 friends each have 3 buns.
   How many buns do they have in total?
   ☐

4. A ruler costs 4p.
   How much would 6 rulers cost?
   ☐ p

Write the answers to the questions below.
See how fast you can do them all.

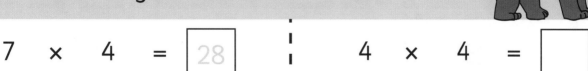

| 7 × 4 = 28 | 4 × 4 = ☐ |
| ☐ × 3 = 12 | ☐ × 4 = 32 |
| 4 × ☐ = 24 | 10 × ☐ = 40 |
| 4 × 2 = ☐ | 12 × 4 = ☐ |
| 9 × ☐ = 36 | ☐ × 1 = 4 |
| ☐ × 5 = 20 | 4 × ☐ = 44 |

# Mixed Questions

Colour in every number that is in the two times table.  See if you can spot a pattern.

| 1 | 2 | 3 | 4 | 5 |
|---|---|---|---|---|
| 6 | 7 | 8 | 9 | 10 |
| 11 | 12 | 13 | 14 | 15 |
| 16 | 17 | 18 | 19 | 20 |
| 21 | 22 | 23 | 24 | 25 |

Draw a ring around the multiplication that matches each number on the left.

| | | | | |
|---|---|---|---|---|
| (35) | (7 × 5) | 10 × 3 | 8 × 4 | 10 × 7 |
| (15) | 3 × 5 | 10 × 4 | 3 × 7 | 5 × 9 |
| (30) | 4 × 3 | 3 × 9 | 8 × 5 | 5 × 6 |
| (27) | 4 × 4 | 3 × 7 | 3 × 9 | 8 × 2 |
| (8) | 3 × 1 | 2 × 4 | 2 × 3 | 5 × 5 |
| (33) | 11 × 3 | 3 × 8 | 2 × 10 | 7 × 3 |

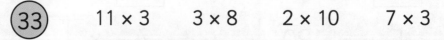

Fill in the boxes to show each number on the clock multiplied by 5.

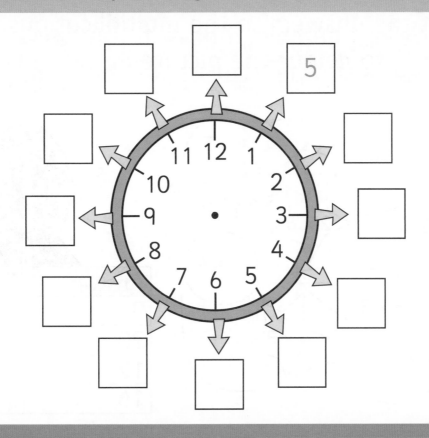

Fill in the boxes to show how many legs are in each set below.

 3 legs

 3 lots of 3 3 × 3 = 9

 ☐ lots of 3 ☐ × ☐ = ☐

 ☐ lots of 3 ☐ × ☐ = ☐

 ☐ lot of 3 ☐ × ☐ = ☐

# Mixed Questions

Work out the answers to the multiplications below.
Use the key to colour the picture in.

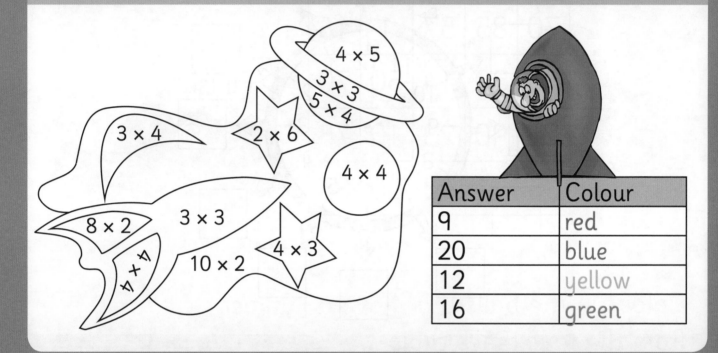

| Answer | Colour |
|--------|--------|
| 9 | red |
| 20 | blue |
| 12 | yellow |
| 16 | green |

Fill in the multiplication table.

| ×  | 1  | 2  | 3  | 4  | 5  | 6  | 7  | 8  | 9  | 10 | 11 | 12 |
|----|----|----|----|----|----|----|----|----|----|----|----|----|
| 2  | 2  |    |    |    |    |    |    | 16 |    | 20 |    |    |
| 3  |    |    | 9  |    |    |    | 21 |    |    |    |    |    |
| 4  | 4  |    |    |    |    | 24 |    |    |    |    |    |    |
| 5  |    | 10 |    |    |    |    |    |    |    |    |    | 60 |
| 10 |    |    |    | 40 |    |    | 70 |    |    |    |    |    |

Draw a line from the start to the finish. Only go through numbers in the ten times table.

Start ⟹

| 10 | 5 | 23 | 29 | 19 |
| 70 | 85 | 57 | 1 | 16 |
| 40 | 30 | 14 | 50 | 70 |
| 29 | 90 | 23 | 10 | 75 |
| 25 | 20 | 60 | 80 | 35 |

⟹ Finish

Colour in the balls that have a number from the four times table.

44  36  18  32

8  7  24  3

38  26  10

# Mixed Questions

Write the answers in the boxes.

**1** A cake costs 10p.
How much would 7 cakes cost?  p

**2** One mouse eats 4 bits of cheese.
How many bits of cheese would 11 mice eat?

**3** A box has 5 pencils in it.
How many pencils would there be in 4 boxes?

**4** One rabbit eats 3 carrots.
How many carrots will 3 rabbits eat?

Write the answers to the questions below.
See how fast you can do them all.

| 7 × 3 = 21 | 2 × 7 = ☐ |
| ☐ × 9 = 36 | ☐ × 8 = 32 |
| 5 × ☐ = 15 | 10 × ☐ = 70 |
| 3 × 12 = ☐ | 4 × 3 = ☐ |
| 6 × ☐ = 24 | ☐ × 9 = 27 |
| ☐ × 5 = 30 | 5 × ☐ = 55 |